Big and L

Story by Joy Cowley

Big ducks have little ducks —
ducklings!

Big cats have little cats –
kittens!

Big dogs have little dogs –
puppies!

4

Big pigs have little pigs –
piglets!

Big bears have little bears –
cubs!

Big people have little people –

children!